School Trouble

Written by Narinder Dhami

Contents

How to Read the Plays 3

Football Crazy 4

The Bully 19

Copycat 35

How to Read the Plays

There are three plays in this book for you to read aloud in a small group. There are six characters in each play.

1   Choose a character.

2   Look through the play at your character's lines.

3   Read your lines quietly to yourself.

4   Read the whole play aloud in your group.

Reading tips

- Follow the play carefully, even when it is not your turn to read.

- Read your lines clearly.

- Try to speak in the way your character would. If you think your character is loud and bossy, then read your part in a loud, bossy voice.

Football Crazy

A Play by Narinder Dhami

Illustrations by David Kearney

Cast

Narrator

Tom

Leroy

Alex

Miss Bond

Mr Sims

Football Crazy
Act I

Narrator *Tom, Leroy and Alex were playing football in the playground before school.*

Tom Pass the ball to me, Alex!

Narrator *Alex passed the ball to Tom, and Tom kicked it as hard as he could. Leroy tried to stop the ball, but he was too slow.*

Tom Yes!

Leroy Great goal, Tom!

Narrator   *Just then the bell rang. Tom pulled a face.*

Tom   Oh no! I don't want to go in. I want to play football.

Alex   You're football mad! You want to play all the time!

Narrator   *Tom, Leroy and Alex went into school. But Tom didn't pick his football up. He kicked it through the door.*

Tom   And here comes Tom! He's going to score a goal for England!

Leroy   Pick the ball up, Tom, or you'll get told off!

Narrator   *But Tom didn't pick the ball up. He kicked it again, and it hit the bookcase!*

Tom And Tom scores a great goal!
England lead 1–0!

Narrator *Just then Miss Bond, the headteacher,*
saw Tom. She was very cross.

Miss Bond Tom! Pick that ball up, please. I've told
you before. It isn't safe to play football
inside. If I catch you again, I'll take
your ball away.

Tom Sorry, Miss Bond.

Narrator *Tom picked up the football. But when*
Miss Bond had gone, he put it
down again and began to kick it.

Leroy Stop it, Tom!

Narrator *But Tom didn't stop. He kicked the ball harder, and it hit the classroom door! Their teacher, Mr Sims, came out.*

Mr Sims I've told you before about playing with your football inside, Tom. If I see it in school again, I will take it away.

Tom Sorry, Mr Sims.

Narrator *Tom went to put his football away. Then the class wrote a story. Tom hated writing. He wanted to play football. He couldn't wait for playtime.*

Mr Sims Put your work away now, please. I have some good news for you.

Narrator *Everyone put their work away. They all wanted to know the good news.*

Mr Sims We have a new computer.

Leroy A new computer! Cool!

Alex I can't wait to have a go!

Tom I hope I can play football games on it!

Narrator *The door opened, and Miss Bond came in with the new computer.*

Miss Bond Here you are, Class 4. I have set the computer up for you. All you have to do is turn it on.

Narrator *Just then the bell rang for playtime.*

Mr Sims Off you go. You can all have a
go on the computer after playtime.

Narrator *Everyone went out to play. Tom went
to get his football. He began to
kick it round the classroom.*

Tom I wish I could play football all the time!

Narrator *But then Tom kicked the ball too hard.
It went over Mr Sim's desk, and it
hit the new computer!*

Act 2

Tom Oh no! The ball has hit the new computer.

Narrator *Tom ran over to the computer and looked at it.*

Tom I hope it's not broken! I'd better try it.

Narrator *Tom tried to turn the computer on. But it wouldn't start. He tried again. But he couldn't get the computer to work.*

Tom Oh no! I've broken the new computer! Mr Sims and Miss Bond are going to be mad! What shall I do?

Narrator *Tom knew that he should own up, but he was scared. No one had seen him. So he grabbed his football and ran out.*

Leroy Where have you been, Tom?

Alex We want to play football.

Tom OK.

Narrator *Tom played football with Leroy and Alex, but he felt very bad about the computer.*

Leroy It will be great to have a new computer in our classroom.

Alex Yes. The old computer was rubbish!

Narrator *Tom felt very upset. Everyone was so pleased about the new computer. What would they do when they found out it was broken?*

Leroy There's the bell. Come on, let's go in.

Alex Yes. Then we'll be first on the computer! Come on, Tom!

Tom I don't want to go on the computer.

Leroy Don't be silly, Tom! Come on.

Narrator *Tom felt scared as they went into class. Soon everyone would know what he had done.*

Mr Sims Leroy and Alex, you can have the first go on the new computer.

Narrator *Leroy and Alex were pleased. They ran over to the computer.*

Narrator   Miss Bond tried to turn the computer on. But it wouldn't start. She tried again and again. But the computer wouldn't come on.

Miss Bond   It's not working. That's very odd.

Narrator   Tom didn't say anything. He didn't know what to do.

Mr Sims   It must be broken.

Miss Bond   But it's a new computer. It can't be broken!

Narrator   Tom felt very bad indeed. He knew that he had to own up.

Act 3

Narrator *Tom got up out of his seat. He went over to Miss Bond.*

Tom Miss Bond, I know why the computer doesn't work.

Miss Bond I don't think you do, Tom.

Tom But I do.

Mr Sims Don't be silly, Tom.

Tom It was me. I broke the computer.

Miss Bond What?

Mr Sims What?

Narrator *Tom felt very upset. Everyone was looking at him.*

Leroy   *You* broke the computer, Tom?

Alex   How did you do that?

Tom   I was kicking my football around the classroom, and it hit the computer! I'm really sorry.

Miss Bond   Tom, how many times have we told you not to play football in school?

Mr Sims   You're a very disobedient boy.

Miss Bond   And now look what you have done. You have broken the new computer!

Mr Sims   Computers cost a lot of money.

Now we will have to get it fixed.

Tom   I'm sorry.

Miss Bond   Well, at least we know why it doesn't

work now.

Mr Sims   Tom, you must not bring your football to

school for the rest of the term. And you

will not go outside at playtime for two

weeks. You will stay in the classroom

with me!

Narrator   *Just then Tom saw something.*

Tom   Miss Bond! Look!

Miss Bond   What is it, Tom?

Tom   The computer is not

plugged in!

Narrator *Miss Bond looked under the desk. Tom was right. She had not plugged the computer in!*

Miss Bond So that was why the computer would not come on!

Narrator *Miss Bond put the plug in and turned it on. The computer lit up.*

Alex The computer's on!

Leroy It's working!

Narrator *Tom felt much better. He hadn't broken the computer after all.*

Miss Bond Well done, Tom. At least the computer isn't broken. But I hope you have learned your lesson. You must not play with your football inside school.

Tom I won't!

The Bully

A Play by Narinder Dhami

Illustrations by Aldo Balding

Cast

Narrator

Mark

Adam

Kelly

Nico

Miss Lee

The Bully
Act I

Narrator *It was Mark's first day at his new school. He watched the children playing in the playground. He wanted to join in, but he didn't know anyone.*

Narrator *Just then a boy ran into the playground. Mark saw a comic fall out of the boy's bag, but the boy didn't see it.*

Mark Hey! You've dropped your comic!

Narrator *The boy didn't stop. He went off to play football. Mark picked up the comic and ran after him.*

Mark   Hey! This is your comic!

Adam   Give it to me! Did you
take it out of my bag?

Mark   No, I didn't. It fell out. Here you are.

Adam   Thanks. I haven't seen you before.
Are you new?

Mark   Yes, I'm Mark.

Adam   I'm Adam. Whose class are you in?

Mark   Miss Lee's class.

Adam   So am I. Do you want to play football?

Mark   Yes.

Narrator   *Mark felt a lot better. Now he
had someone to play with.
Just then the school bell rang.*

Adam   We've got to go in now. I'll show
you where to go.

Mark   Can I sit next to you in class?

Adam   Yes, and we can play football together
at playtime.

Mark   I've got some crisps for playtime.
I'll share them with you.

Adam   I can get lots of sweets for us. It's easy.

Narrator   *Adam saw some little children going
into school. He went over to them.*

Adam   Who's got any sweets on them?
Hand them over. Hurry up!

Mark   You can't take their sweets!

Adam   Yes, I can! I do it all the time.

Narrator   *Just then Nico and Kelly came running over.*

Nico   What's going on?

Kelly   What are you doing with the little children?

Adam   Get lost, you two!

Nico   Miss Lee sent us to find the new boy.

Adam   Go away, Nico. Mark is *my* friend.
I will take him to Miss Lee.
Push off, or I'll kick you!

Narrator   *Nico and Kelly ran off. Mark wasn't very happy. He wasn't so sure he wanted to be Adam's friend after all.*

Act 2

Narrator *The children went into the classroom. Mark didn't want to sit next to Adam, but Adam grabbed him.*

Adam You're *my* friend. You must sit next to *me*.

Narrator *Miss Lee came over to see what was going on.*

Miss Lee Hello. You must be Mark. We are very pleased to have you in our class. Where would you like to sit?

Adam   Mark wants to sit next to me.

Miss Lee   Is that what you want, Mark?

Narrator   *Mark didn't want to sit next to Adam,*
but he was too afraid to say so.

Mark   Yes, Miss.

Narrator   *Mark sat down and tried to do his work,*
but Adam kept messing around.

Miss Lee   Be quiet, you two, and get on with
your work.

Mark   Yes, Miss.

Adam   It will be playtime soon. Then we can
play football, and I can get some
more sweets!

Miss Lee   OK, class. Put your books away, please. I want to talk to you before you go out to play.

Narrator   *Everyone put their books away.*

Miss Lee   I want to talk to you about bullying.

Narrator   *Nico and Kelly looked at Mark.*
Mark went red.

Miss Lee   You all know that we don't like bullies in this school. But someone is taking sweets from the little children.
Does anyone know who the bully is?

Narrator   *Mark wanted say that Adam was the bully, but he was afraid of Adam.*

Miss Lee   If I find out that anyone in this
class has been bullying, then they
will be in *big* trouble.

Narrator   *Nico and Kelly looked at Mark again.*
Mark didn't know what to do. If he told
Miss Lee about Adam, then Nico
and Kelly might be his friends, but what
would Adam do to him?

Miss Lee   Have you seen any bullying in the
playground, Nico?

Nico   No, Miss.

Miss Lee   What about you, Kelly?

Kelly   No, Miss.

Narrator   *Mark could see that Nico and*
Kelly were afraid too. No one wanted
to tell Miss Lee what was going on.

Miss Lee   *I want you all to keep a look out.*
If you see any bullying in school,
come and tell me.

Narrator   *Then the bell rang. Everyone went*
out to play.

Adam   See, Mark? No one told Miss Lee that
I took the sweets! Everyone is afraid
of me!

Mark   Come on. Let's go and play football.

Adam   No. I have to get some sweets first.

Narrator   *Adam looked around the playground.*
He saw Nico and Kelly sitting on
the wall.

Adam   Look! Nico has got a big bar of
chocolate! I'm going to get it!

Act 3

Narrator *Adam went over to Nico to get the bar of chocolate. Mark ran after him.*

Mark You mustn't take any more sweets, Adam! You know what Miss Lee said.

Adam I want that bar of chocolate, Nico. Give it to me, or I'll kick you!

Nico No, way!

Kelly Go away, Adam, or we'll tell Miss Lee!

Adam No, you won't! Give me the chocolate!

Narrator *Adam grabbed the bar of chocolate from Nico, and ran off. Mark didn't know what to do. Should he go and get Miss Lee? Should he try to stop Adam himself?*

Mark Give it back, Adam!

Narrator *Mark ran after Adam, and grabbed the bar of chocolate!*

Adam Hey! What are you doing?

Mark I'm going to give the chocolate back to Nico.

Narrator *Adam tried to grab the chocolate bar. He and Mark didn't see Miss Lee coming over to them.*

Miss Lee What's going on here?

Nico That's my bar of chocolate, Miss!

Miss Lee Why has Mark got it then? Did you take it from Nico, Mark?

Mark No, Miss!

Miss Lee I'm very cross with you, Mark. I will not have bullying in this school.

Mark But it wasn't me, Miss!

Narrator *Mark looked at Adam, but Adam didn't say anything. He wasn't going to own up.*

Miss Lee Give the bar of chocolate back to Nico, and come into school with me. I will have to take you to the headteacher.

HEADTEACHER

Narrator *Mark was very upset. It was his first day at his new school, and he was in trouble. As Miss Lee led Mark into school, Adam called after them.*

Adam It wasn't Mark, Miss. It was me.

Miss Lee Is this true?

Nico Yes, Miss. It was Adam.

Kelly Mark was trying to help us to get the chocolate back.

Miss Lee Let's all go into school and sort this out.

Narrator *Miss Lee took them all into school. First she talked to Adam on his own. Then she talked to Mark, Nico and Kelly.*

Miss Lee   Adam has done some bad things,
but he has owned up at last.
Sometimes a bully needs our help to
stop what he is doing.

Nico   What can we do, Miss?

Miss Lee   I know it won't be easy. But the best
thing you can do is be his friend.

Mark   I'm not sure that I want to be his friend.

Miss Lee   If Adam has good friends like you,
I think he will stop bullying.
Will you help him?

**Mark,
Nico
and Kelly**   We'll try.

33

Narrator   *Mark, Nico and Kelly went into the playground. Adam was there.*

Adam   I'm sorry I took your chocolate, Nico.

Narrator   *Mark, Nico and Kelly didn't want to be friends with Adam. But Miss Lee had asked them to help him, so they had to try.*

Nico   Everyone can have some of my chocolate.

Mark   And then we can all play football.

Adam   Great!

Narrator   *Mark was very pleased. Now he had three friends. Not bad for a new boy!*

Copycat

A Play by Narinder Dhami
Illustrations by Karin Littlewood

Cast

Narrator

Kim

Robin

Mr Davis

Mr Sharma

Simon

Copycat
Act 1

Narrator	*Kim and Robin were twins. They were in the same class at school.*
Kim	Oh no! It's maths first thing. I *hate* maths!
Robin	I *love* maths!
Narrator	*Just then Simon came and sat down. Simon was Robin's best friend.*
Simon	Hi, you two.
Kim and Robin	Hi, Simon.
Mr Davis	OK, everyone! It's time for some maths.

Narrator   *Mr Davis tested the children on their tables. Then they had to do some sums in their books. Kim didn't know how to do the sums.*

Mr Davis   Kim, bring your maths book to me, please.

Kim   Oh no!

Narrator   *Kim took her maths book to Mr Davis and he looked at her sums. Kim had got all the sums wrong.*

Mr Davis   You'll have to do these again, Kim. Let me show you how to do them.

Narrator *Mr Davis told Kim how to do the sums, but Kim wasn't listening.*

Robin Look at Kim! She's not listening!

Simon That's why she doesn't know how to do the sums!

Mr Davis Try these sums again, Kim.

Narrator *Kim went back to her table, looking very cross.*

Kim I'm fed up! I got all the sums wrong. Now I've got to do them again, and I don't know how.

Robin   But Mr Davis just told you.
You weren't listening!

Narrator   *Just then the door opened. Mr Sharma,*
the headteacher, came in.

Mr Sharma   How nice to see everyone working so
hard. Mr Davis, can I have a word
with you, please?

Kim   Hey, Robin! Mr Davis isn't looking.
Do my sums for me!

Robin   No, I'd better not.

Kim   Oh, go on, Robin! Please!

Narrator   *Kim pushed her book over to Robin.*
Robin did the sums quickly and pushed
the book back to Kim.

Act 2

Narrator   *Mr Davis and Mr Sharma came over to Kim's table.*

Mr Sharma   I can see that everyone on this table is working very hard.

Narrator   *Mr Sharma looked at Robin's book.*

Mr Sharma   Well, done, Robin! You've got all your work right. And so has Simon.

Kim   Mr Davis, I've done all my sums again.

Mr Davis   That was quick! I'll mark them for you.

Narrator   *Mr Davis marked Kim's sums.*

Mr Davis Well done, Kim! I knew you could get them right!

Narrator *Kim was pleased, but Robin felt bad. Mr Davis would be very cross if he knew that Robin had done all the sums.*

Mr Davis I think I'll give Kim a gold star. What do you think, Mr Sharma?

Mr Sharma Yes, she's worked hard today.

Narrator *Mr Davis stuck a gold star in Kim's maths book. Everyone in the class clapped and cheered. Kim was very pleased.*

Mr Sharma I will come back tomorrow to see how Kim is getting on with her maths.

Narrator *Mr Sharma went out, and Mr Davis went back to his desk.*

Kim   I got a gold star! I got a gold star!

Simon   Robin was the one who did the sums. Give him the gold star!

Kim   No way! It's mine!

Narrator   *Then Mr Davis came over to them again.*

Mr Davis   I would like you to try some harder sums now, Kim. Here you are.

Kim   Oh! OK, Mr Davis.

Narrator   *Mr Davis went back to his desk. Kim looked at the sums, and her eyes nearly popped out.*

Kim   I can't do these! They're much
         too hard!

Robin   Well, I'm not doing them!

Kim   Oh, go on, Robin! Help me!

Robin   No, I can't! Mr Davis will see, and then
           we'll both be in trouble!

Kim   Please, Robin. Mr Sharma is going to
         come back to see how I'm getting on.
         I've got to get the sums right!

Simon   Don't do it, Robin!

Narrator   *Robin didn't know what to do.*
              He didn't want to get into
              trouble with Mr Sharma, but he
              wanted to help Kim.

Robin   OK. I'll do them for you.

43

Act 3

Narrator   *It was the next day and Robin was feeling fed up. They had maths again first thing, and he knew Kim would want him to do all her sums.*

Simon   Just tell Kim that you won't do her maths anymore.

Robin   But she's my twin.

Simon   You are going to get found out and then you'll both be in trouble.

Narrator   *Robin knew that Simon was right. But it seemed mean not to help his twin sister.*

Kim You will help me with my sums today, won't you, Robin? Mr Sharma will be coming back to see how I'm doing.

Robin I can't do your sums all the time, Kim!

Kim Why not?

Robin Because Mr Davis will find out.

Mr Davis Get your maths books out everyone. Mr Sharma will be here soon.

Narrator *Robin loved maths, but today he didn't feel like doing sums at all. He was worried that Mr Sharma would find out about the copying.*

Mr Davis Robin and Kim, I would like you both to do the same sums today. They are hard, but I think you can do them.

Narrator *Just then Mr Sharma came in.*

Mr Sharma I see I'm just in time for maths.
How is Kim getting on?

Mr Davis Kim and Robin are doing the same
sums today.

Mr Sharma Very good. I'm sure they'll both get
them right.

Narrator *Robin let Kim copy his sums.*
Mr Davis marked Robin's sums first.
Seven of the sums were right but three
of them were wrong!

Mr Davis That's not like you, Robin. You'll have
to try those three sums again.

Narrator *Then Mr Davis marked Kim's sums.*

Mr Davis That's very odd. Kim has the same
sums wrong. Someone has
been copying!

Narrator *Mr Sharma and Mr Davis looked at Kim and Robin.*

Kim It was me! I asked Robin to let me copy his sums because I couldn't do them.

Mr Davis What a silly thing to do. I'm very cross with both of you!

Mr Sharma So am I! You won't get better at maths if you copy Robin's work, Kim.

Kim I'm sorry.

Robin Me too.

Mr Davis Well, you have owned up, which is a good thing. But I think Kim needs some more help with her maths.

Mr Sharma Yes. Kim can come to my room every playtime and do some maths with me.

Narrator *Mr Davis and Mr Sharma went away.*

Kim Oh no! Maths with Mr Sharma!

Robin At least *I* don't have to do your maths anymore!

Mr Davis OK, everyone. Put your maths books away. Now we're going to write a story.

Robin Oh no! I *hate* writing stories!

Kim I *love* writing stories!